What Can We in Winter?

by Caroline Hutchinson

We see ice on the pond.

We can skate.

We see snow in the yard.

We can make a snowman.

4

We see snow on the hill.
We can go sledding.

We see snow on the mountain.
We can go skiing.

We see snow in the park.

We can make snow angels.

We see snow in the field.

We can make a fort.

We see snow everywhere.

We can play games inside!